The Best
HOLIDAY
Ever

My family's very busy.
We always rush about.

Mum is coming in

when Dad is going out.

Charlie has his friends.

Grandma never takes it slow.

We need a great holiday,

but we don't know where to go.

Maybe if I ask some questions

and write down the answers, too—

then we'll have some charts

that will tell us what to do.

Should we go somewhere warm?

Should we travel somewhere far?

What about excitement?

Could Fluffer come with us?

	warm	cool
Mum		×
Dad	×	
Grandma	×	
Charlie	×	
Me	×	
	④	1

	far	near
Mum		X
Dad		X
Grandma		X
Charlie	X	
Me	X	
	2	③

	fun	quiet
Mum		X
Dad		X
Grandma	X	
Charlie	X	
Me	X	
	③	2

	no	Fluffer
Mum		X
Dad	X	
Grandma		X
Charlie		X
Me		X
	1	④

Now I'll add my numbers
and see just what they show.

After looking at my charts,

I know exactly where to go!

warm
near
fun
Fluffer

To find the perfect place

wasn't really very hard.

Our best holiday ever is right here in our back yard!

ACTIVITIES AT SCHOOL

The following activities will help you to extend children's understanding of the concepts presented in *The Best Holiday Ever*:

• Read the story with the children and ask them to describe what is happening in each picture. Talk about the questions the girl is asking and the answers that her family give.

• Discuss what the girl learns from each of the charts she makes. Ask questions throughout the story, such as 'Do more people want to go somewhere warm or cool? Do more people want to stay near or go far?'

• Ask the children to answer the girl's questions: 'How about you? Would you rather take a holiday somewhere warm or cool? Somewhere exciting or quiet?'

• Together think of some questions that might help members of the children's families decide where to go for their holidays. Write the questions down. Then help the children ask the questions and record the answers in simple charts. Review the charts together and discuss what would be a good holiday destination.

ACTIVITIES AT HOME

If you would like to have fun with the maths concepts presented in *The Best Holiday Ever*, here are a few suggestions:

- After reading the story with your child, ask him or her to retell it in his or her own words.

- Look around your neighbourhood and ask what things more people like. For example, what sort of cars do people drive – big or small? What is the most popular colour for a car? What sort of footwear do most children wear, shoes or trainers? Help your child to record this information and then discuss the answers to the questions.

- Plan a picnic together. What questions would you ask to find out each person's favourite foods? How would you record the information? Can you decide upon a menu that most people would like?

- Together make a family chart. Are there more females or males in your family? Are there more people with blue eyes or brown eyes? Do most people have the same colour hair?